Marie Lallaway, Tom Johns and Mig Bennett

Rising Stars UK Ltd, 22 Grafton Street, London W1S 4EX

www.risingstars-uk.com

Published 2010

Editorial: Sandra Stafford
Illustrations: Phill Burrows
Design: Branford Graphics and Clive Sutherland
Cover design: Burville-Riley Partnership

Text acknowledgements
p15 Extract adapted from *Pirates* by Celia Ress, Bloomsbury; p38 Extract from *Kennedy for the Defense: A Novel* by George V. Higgins; p39 Extract from *Of Mice and Men* by John Steinbeck.

British Library Cataloguing in Publication Data.
A CIP record for this book is available from the British Library.

ISBN: 978 1 84680 685 8

Printed by Craft Print International Ltd, Singapore

Contents

What are writing skills?

Did you know that teachers are helping you to develop your writing in at least seven different ways? These are called 'assessment focuses' (AFs). They are described here:

- ★ **AF1:** Write imaginative, interesting and thoughtful texts.
- ★ **AF2:** Produce texts which are appropriate to task, reader and purpose.
- ★ **AF3:** Organise and present whole texts effectively, sequencing and structuring information, ideas and events.
- ★ **AF4:** Construct paragraphs and use cohesion within and between paragraphs.
- ★ **AF5:** Vary sentences for clarity, purpose and effect.
- ★ **AF6:** Write with technical accuracy of syntax and punctuation in phrases, clauses and sentences.
- ★ **AF7:** Select appropriate and effective vocabulary.

The AFs can be grouped together, like this, to make them more manageable to practise:

Sentences:	Construct complex sentences, including use of connectives, adjectives, adverbs and punctuation.		AF5/6/7
Paragraphs:	Organise your writing.		AF3/4
Whole text:	Develop ideas, think about the needs of a reader, use interesting vocabulary and an appropriate style.	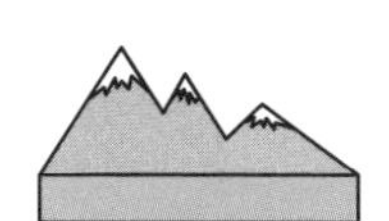	AF1/2

These writing skills fit together, like bricks in a wall, to make your written work strong and successful.

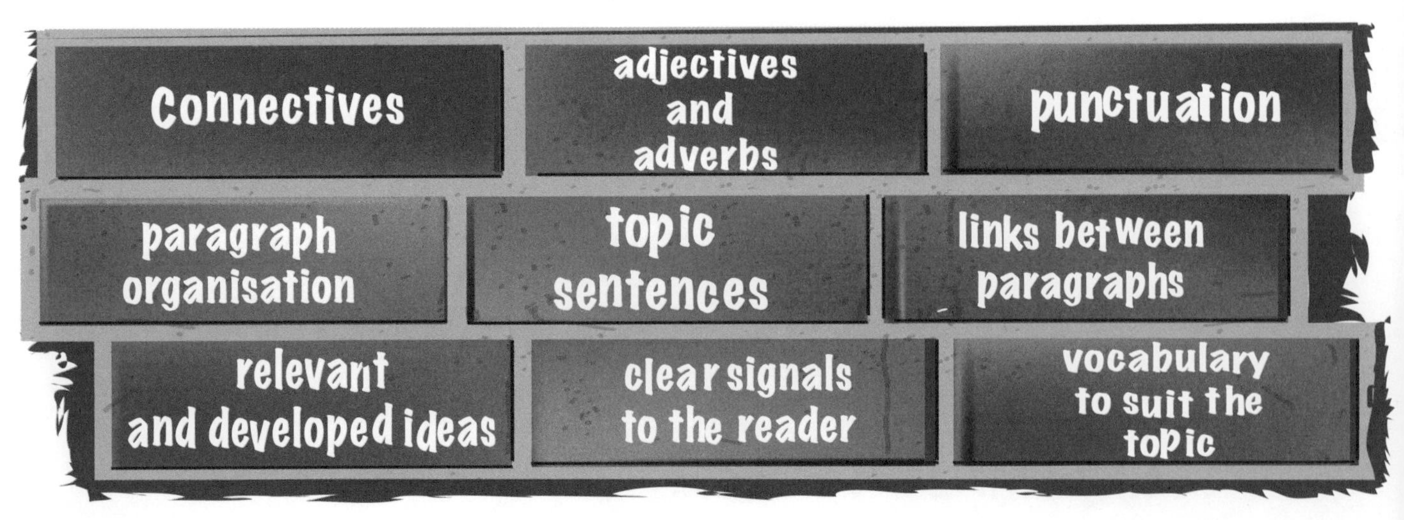

Why use this book?

This book will help you to move your writing skills up from one National Curriculum level to another. For example, if you are currently working at level 5, advice and exercises will help you to progress to level 6, or 7.

- **Knowing what you need to do** to achieve your target level is also essential so we explain and give examples of what you need to be able to do.
- We know that students **learn by doing** so practice is an important part of the book.

The book includes the following features to make it easy to use and to highlight what you really need to be able to do.

1. **Target level statement** – this tells you what you need to do to achieve the next level in your reading skill.
2. **Assessment focus** – this identifies the main writing skill that is being practised. See page 4 for more information.
3. **Tips** – these give you helpful hints, similar to how your teacher does in class.
4. **Writing practice tasks** – varied exercises to help you practise language skills.

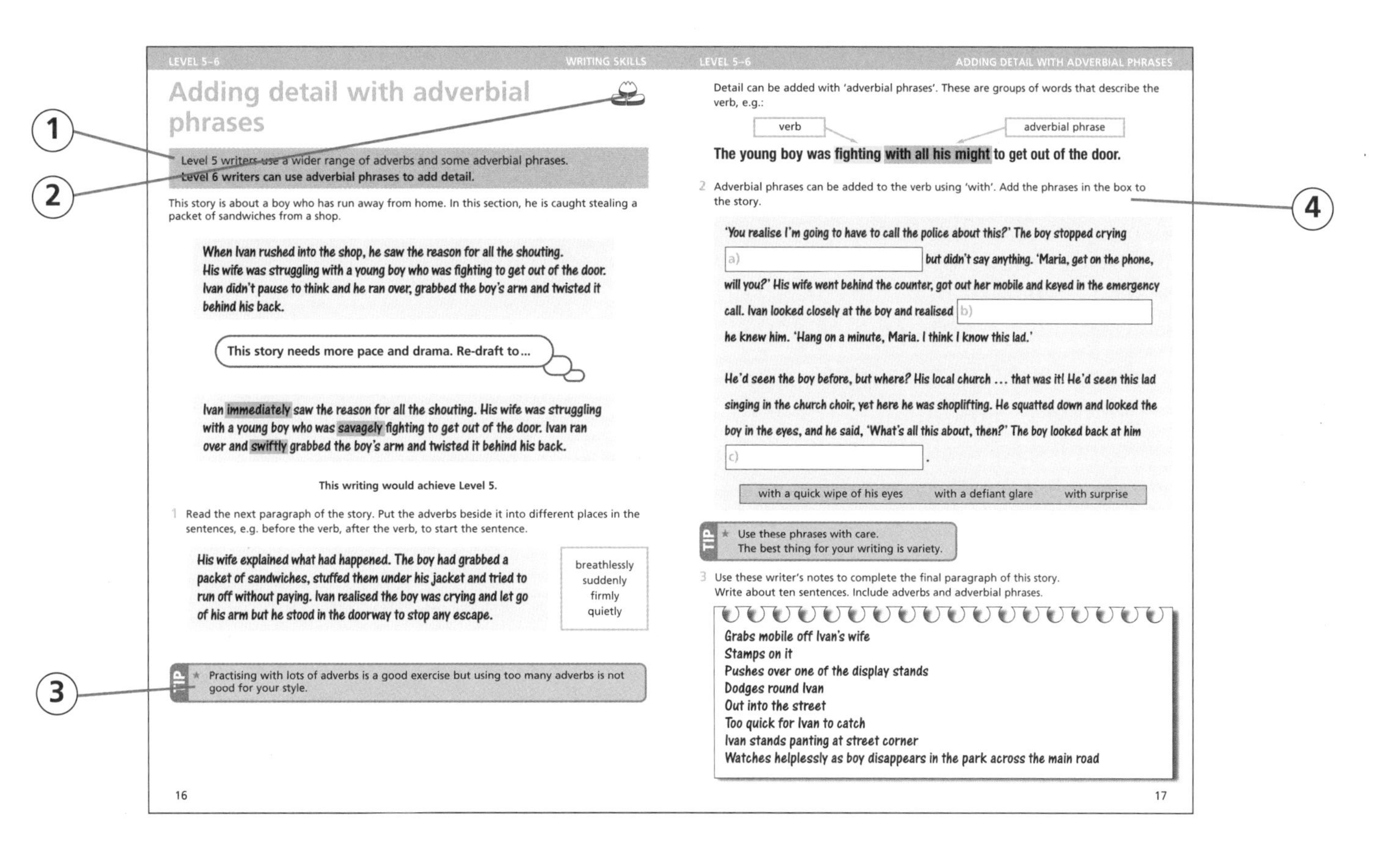

LEVEL 5–6 WRITING SKILLS

Adding detail with adverbial phrases

Level 5 writers use a wider range of adverbs and some adverbial phrases.
Level 6 writers can use adverbial phrases to add detail.

This story is about a boy who has run away from home. In this section, he is caught stealing a packet of sandwiches from a shop.

When Ivan rushed into the shop, he saw the reason for all the shouting. His wife was struggling with a young boy who was fighting to get out of the door. Ivan didn't pause to think and he ran over, grabbed the boy's arm and twisted it behind his back.

This story needs more pace and drama. Re-draft to…

Ivan immediately saw the reason for all the shouting. His wife was struggling with a young boy who was savagely fighting to get out of the door. Ivan ran over and swiftly grabbed the boy's arm and twisted it behind his back.

This writing would achieve Level 5.

1 Read the next paragraph of the story. Put the adverbs beside it into different places in the sentences, e.g. before the verb, after the verb, to start the sentence.

His wife explained what had happened. The boy had grabbed a packet of sandwiches, stuffed them under his jacket and tried to run off without paying. Ivan realised the boy was crying and let go of his arm but he stood in the doorway to stop any escape.

breathlessly
suddenly
firmly
quietly

TIP ★ Practising with lots of adverbs is a good exercise but using too many adverbs is not good for your style.

16

LEVEL 5–6 ADDING DETAIL WITH ADVERBIAL PHRASES

Detail can be added with 'adverbial phrases'. These are groups of words that describe the verb, e.g.:

verb — adverbial phrase

The young boy was fighting with all his might to get out of the door.

2 Adverbial phrases can be added to the verb using 'with'. Add the phrases in the box to the story.

'You realise I'm going to have to call the police about this?' The boy stopped crying a) ______ but didn't say anything. 'Maria, get on the phone, will you?' His wife went behind the counter, got out her mobile and keyed in the emergency call. Ivan looked closely at the boy and realised b) ______ he knew him. 'Hang on a minute, Maria. I think I know this lad.'

He'd seen the boy before, but where? His local church … that was it! He'd seen this lad singing in the church choir, yet here he was shoplifting. He squatted down and looked the boy in the eyes, and he said, 'What's all this about, then?' The boy looked back at him c) ______.

with a quick wipe of his eyes | with a defiant glare | with surprise

TIP ★ Use these phrases with care. The best thing for your writing is variety.

3 Use these writer's notes to complete the final paragraph of this story. Write about ten sentences. Include adverbs and adverbial phrases.

Grabs mobile off Ivan's wife
Stamps on it
Pushes over one of the display stands
Dodges round Ivan
Out into the street
Too quick for Ivan to catch
Ivan stands panting at street corner
Watches helplessly as boy disappears in the park across the main road

17

How to use this book

- You can use the sections in this book to work on the writing skills you need to practise. Or, work through the whole book for overall improvement. The following sections will help you to practise one skill at a time. This approach helps you to focus closely on each element of writing so that you can improve your overall standard of writing when you combine all the skills together.
- Each section targets a different writing skill and practises the skill in a variety of ways across levels 5, 6 and 7 so that you can learn the 'extra' things you need to understand and do for each level.
- Practise in short bursts of activity and **do** read the advice first so that you focus on the writing skill, not just answering the questions.
- 'Warm up' by doing an exercise at your current writing level before trying the exercises to move you up to the next level.
- Use the **self-assessment sheets** on pages 44 and 45 to identify the level at which you are writing.

Sentence structure and punctuation

- **Connectives** (pages 8–11) writers at:
  Level 5 use a variety of connectives and sometimes use them to begin a sentence.
  Level 6 select appropriate connectives to help the reader make links between ideas.
  Level 7 use connectives precisely to draw attention to links between ideas.
- **Adjectives** (pages 12–15) writers at:
  Level 5 add detail with interesting adjectives and longer phrases and clauses.
  Level 6 add detail with well-selected words and phrases.
  Level 7 add detail and interest with a wide range of descriptive words and phrases.
- **Adverbs** (pages 16–19) writers at:
  Level 5 use a wider range of adverbs and some adverbial phrases.
  Level 6 can use adverbial phrases to add detail.
  Level 7 can use adverbial phrases to add precise detail to their writing.
- **Punctuation** (pages 20–23) writers at:
  Level 5 use a wider range of punctuation accurately.
  Level 6 use a full range of punctuation accurately.
  Level 7 use punctuation to make meaning clear, and for effect.

Text structure and organisation

- **Paragraph and text organisation devices** (pages 24–27) writers at:
  Level 5 give openings and closing to their work.
  Level 6 give clear openings and closings, and make links between sections.
  Level 7 can use different styles of paragraphs to add interest and impact to their writing.

Using an appropriate style for the task and the reader

Practice and helpful techniques to improve your writing in a range of different styles:

- **Informative writing** (pages 28–31) writers at:
  Level 5 choose language to inform and interest the reader.
  Level 6 use language confidently to convince the reader.
  Level 7 select language and ideas to interest and inform the reader.
- **Persuasive writing** (pages 32–35) writers at:
  Level 5 use some techniques to influence a reader.
  Level 6 can produce persuasive writing using a variety of techniques.
  Level 7 can persuade a reader by choosing information with care and presenting it with style.
- **Imaginative writing** (pages 36–39) writers at:
  Level 5 tell a story, making careful decisions about character and action.
  Level 6 build atmosphere and character in stories with careful choice of words.
  Level 7 can 'show' character and atmosphere through details within the plot.
- **Writing to review** (pages 40–43) writers at:
  Level 5 explain opinions clearly and politely.
  Level 6 explain opinions in detail, using an appropriate tone.
  Level 7 interestingly explain precise opinions.

Developing your writing skills

Understanding **what** to practise is very important to your progress. Use this table to plan your improvement and identify what you want to do first.

		I can	I want to do this			
	skill	**Level 5**	**Level 6**	**pages**	**Level 7**	**pages**
sentences	Connectives	use a variety of connectives and sometimes use them to begin sentences	select appropriate connectives to help the reader make links between ideas	8–9	use connectives precisely to draw attention to links between ideas	10–11
	Adjectives and adverbs	use longer phrases and clauses to add detail and interest	add detail with well-selected words and phrases	12–13 16–17	add detail and interest with a wide range of descriptive words and phrases	14–15 18–19
	Punctuation	use a wider range of punctuation accurately	use a full range of punctuation accurately	20–21	use punctuation to make meaning clear, and for effect	22–23
paragraphs	Paragraph and text organisation	give clear openings and closings to my work	use paragraphs to sequence and control ideas	24–25	use different styles of paragraph to add interest and impact to my writing	26–27
whole text	Informative writing	choose language to inform and interest a reader	select ideas to inform the reader	28–29	select language and ideas to interest and inform the reader	30–31
	Persuasive writing	use some techniques to influence a reader	produce persuasive writing using a variety of techniques	32–33	persuade a reader by choosing information with care and presenting it with passion and style	34–35
	Imaginative writing	tell a story, making careful decisions about character and action	build atmosphere and character in stories with careful choice of words	36–37	'show' character and atmosphere through details within the plot	38–39
	Writing to review	explain opinions clearly and politely	explain opinions precisely	40–41	interestingly explain precise opinions	42–43

Shade each section when you have completed the exercises successfully.

★ Ask your teacher for help in choosing what to do first. Your teacher wants you to improve too.

Using a wider range of connectives 

Level 5 writers use a variety of connectives and sometimes use them to begin a sentence.
Level 6 writers select appropriate connectives to help the reader make links between ideas.

1 Revise the connectives you know how to use.
Imagine you are a young writer working on the opening of a story:
Agent Swift – Special Operations Squad.
Here are some ideas.

Agent Swift was looking at his watch. He heard the shot. He jumped up. He grabbed his gun from the table. He quickly checked the gun was loaded. He ran to the window to look down at the street. The street looked no different. He thought there was something odd about it.

You want to build up the sentences to give more variety. Fill in the gaps with your choice of words.

unless	where	before	although
where	when	although	before
as	wherever	after	until

Agent Swift was looking at his watch a) ______ he heard the the shot. He grabbed his gun from the table b) ______ he jumped up. He quickly checked the gun was loaded c) ______ he ran to the window to look down at the street. The street looked no different d) ______ he thought there was something odd about it.

Although different connectives have been used, they could be better placed to achieve a more interesting effect.

2 Which connectives would you use to open these sentences?

Agent Swift was looking at his watch when he heard the shot.

a) ______ he grabbed his gun from the table, he jumped up.

He quickly checked the gun was loaded before he ran to the window to look down at the street. b) ______ the street looked no different, he thought there was something odd about it.

TIP ★ When you begin a sentence with a connective, use a comma at the end of the first part. If you read the sentence aloud, you can hear a slight pause there.

3 Look at the next part of the story. Practise putting the connectives and commas in the right places.

It was then Agent Swift realised that the trees had no leaves. They were completely bare. a) ______ he had walked down that same street two hours ago every tree was full of fluttering leaves. He looked at the calendar on the office wall to check the date – 10th July. b) ______ he knew it was mid-summer it looked like mid-winter outside!

When **Even though**

TIP ★ Choosing the right place for the connective is important.
If the connective is placed first, attention is focused onto that part of the sentence.

4 Write the next paragraph of the story, trying to include these connectives:

as soon as **before** **while** **whereas** **whoever**

TIP ★ Vary the position of the connective, depending on which piece of information you want to draw attention to.

Level 6 writers select appropriate connectives to help the reader make links between ideas.

Level 7 writers use connectives precisely to draw attention to links between ideas.

5 Read this pupil's work. It is the first draft of a report. The teacher has marked the work with comments A–E. Draw lines to match these comments to the connectives in the text. The colour coding should help you.

TEACHER COMMENTS

A Good variety of connectives used to join sentences.

B Shows you can indicate switch of subject matter in a different way. Glad you remembered both the commas.

C Useful connectives to signal switch of subject matter.

D Good use of connective at start of sentence and you've remembered the comma.

E Fine to use the most common connective – just don't over-use it!

Yesterday's visit by the Stagefight Theatre Company was an unexpected success.
Full marks to Miss Fox for organising it.

Because the theatre companies who visited us last year were so bad, all of the Year 9 Drama group groaned last week when they heard the were in for another 'treat'. Cries of, 'Not another wasted afternoon' and, 'I ain't goin' were heard from the back row of the class. However, the atmosphere changed after it was explained that this company was going to show how stage violence could be made to look real. Some sulky faces suddenly looked curious. The back row, on the other hand, were harder cases and remained unconvinced until it was revealed that volunteers were needed for the swordfight demonstration. Their hands went up as one. Seal of approval given, then.

Meanwhile, we eager swots at the front had grabbed parental consent forms from the desk and were stuffing them in bags as if they were bank notes snatched in a raid. Next week suddenly looked very promising ...

★ Keep up your use of connectives, but remember that sometimes you may want to have a short, simple sentence to create an effect.

6 Read these notes made for the next paragraph of the report.

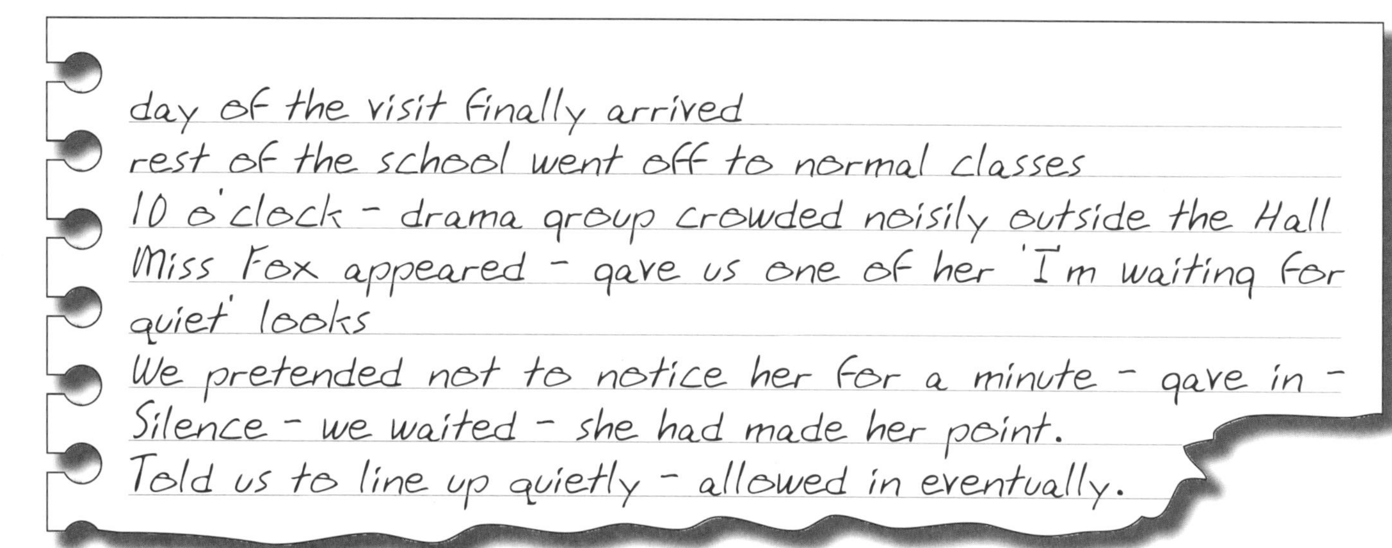
day of the visit finally arrived
rest of the school went off to normal classes
10 o'clock – drama group crowded noisily outside the Hall
Miss Fox appeared – gave us one of her 'I'm waiting for quiet' looks
We pretended not to notice her for a minute – gave in –
Silence – we waited – she had made her point.
Told us to line up quietly – allowed in eventually.

Write up the notes in an interesting paragraph. You might need to add or change a few words but don't add new information. Just practise by using at least five of the connectives from the box. Write two different versions to prove there isn't a right answer!

when	although	until	after	but	however	as	meanwhile

TIP ★ Level 7 writers use connectives for emphasis or suspense, or to control the pace of their writing.

7 Use these notes to create the final paragraphs of the report. Remember to use connectives to create sentence variety and effects such as emphasis and suspense. Also, remember to use a short sentence, too.

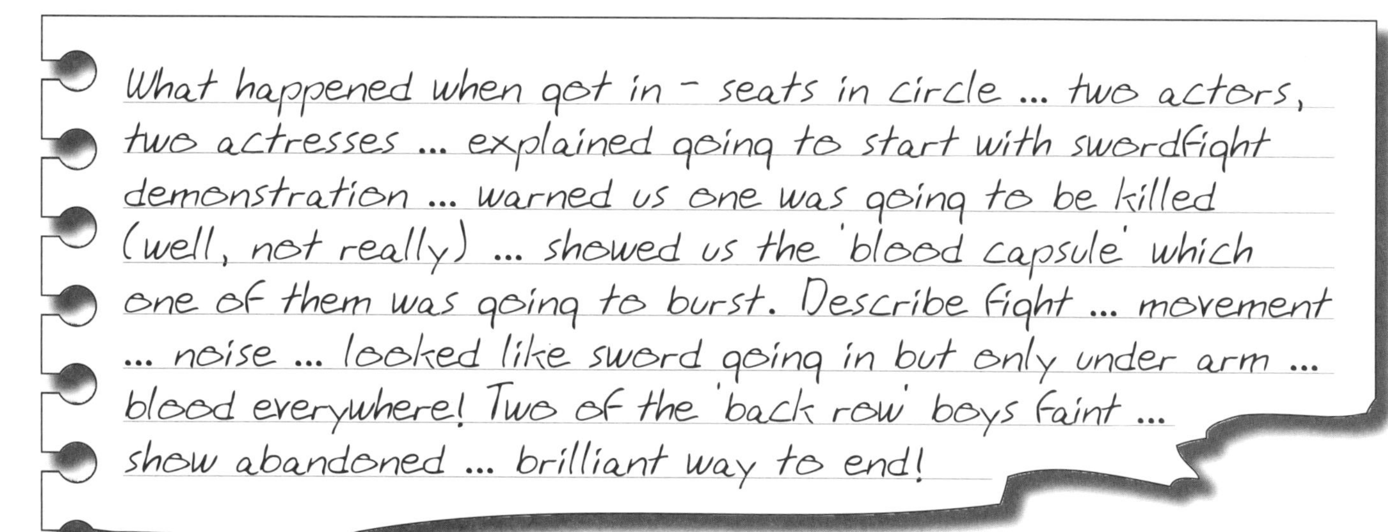
What happened when got in – seats in circle ... two actors, two actresses ... explained going to start with swordfight demonstration ... warned us one was going to be killed (well, not really) ... showed us the 'blood capsule' which one of them was going to burst. Describe fight ... movement ... noise ... looked like sword going in but only under arm ... blood everywhere! Two of the 'back row' boys faint ... show abandoned ... brilliant way to end!

Adding detail with descriptive phrases

Level 5 writers add detail with interesting adjectives and longer phrases and clauses.
Level 6 writers add detail with well-selected words and phrases.

Carefully chosen adjectives, or pairs of adjectives, help to create deliberate effects in your writing.

1 Read this extract from a story. Ignore the numbers for the moment.

> Even though the room was empty, I could still sense her (1) presence. I recalled the look on her (2) face as she turned to face me. I would never forget the sound of her (3) voice as she passed close by on her way out. That (4) smile of hers would stay with me to the end of my days.

Put one adjective by each of the numbers to turn the extract into the start of a romance or a horror story.

ROMANCE	HORROR
(1) ______	(1) ______
(2) ______	(2) ______
(3) ______	(3) ______
(4) ______	(4) ______

Sometimes more than one adjective can be used to intensify the effect you want to create. These can be joined by '*and*' or by a comma, e.g.:

As I left the cold and empty house, I knew I would never return.

As I left the cold, empty house, I knew I would never return.

Doing that too often would be repetitive. It's something to be done selectively.

2 Add another adjective to the ones you have chosen for numbers (1) and (4). Decide whether you want to add a comma or use '*and*'. Do what you think creates the best effect.

3 Consider how you can use alliteration to create an even more noticeable effect. Instead of 'cold and empty', the adjective combination could be:

As I left the cold and cavernous house ...

As I left the eerie, evil-smelling house ...

4 This mystery story needs more detail. Put one single adjective or a set of double adjectives in each sentence. The boxed list is more than you need. There isn't a correct answer; it's up to you to create the effect you want.
Now copy out **your** version of how the story should start.

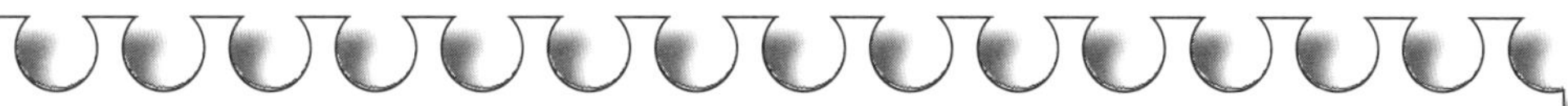

As soon as I had unpacked my case, I could hear voices in the next room. The language intrigued me. The sounds were unlike anything I had heard before. Then the music started. It was the music that awakened a memory in me.

strange, harsh
unearthly
sweet, soft
loud
beautiful
weird
dark and depressing
unpleasant

5 Compare your new version with this one. Yours may be much more interesting!

As soon as I had unpacked my case, I could hear beautiful voices in the next room.
The sweet, soft language intrigued me.
The unearthly sounds were unlike anything I had heard before. Then the weird music started. It was the music which awakened a dark and depressing memory in me.

TIP
★ Remember: adding lots of adjectives doesn't always improve your writing. They have to be well-chosen.

6 Show how well you can use adjectives (and other words!) in your own writing. Pick one topic from below. Then write the first paragraph, using about 100 words. Remember to use:

★ single adjectives;
★ one pair of adjectives;
★ one pair of alliterated adjectives.

Topics

★ A war story
★ A film review
★ A report about a school trip
★ A science-fiction story
★ A description of a sporting event

Level 6 writers add detail with well-selected words and phrases.

Level 7 writers add detail and interest with a wide range of descriptive words and phrases.

Some styles of writing require developed descriptive phrases. Others do not. Description is most evident in imaginative writing, but it exists in other forms of writing in subtle and interesting ways.

7 Review the different types of descriptive phrases used in this example of persuasive writing.

noun

In today's hectic parental schedules, it is easy to overlook the potential damage that overexposure to television can cause to the nation's children. One major disadvantage of our indulgent lifestyles is the excessive amount of time spent sitting, or lying, in front of the 'goggle-box'.

Read the opening of the article, which aims to persuade parents that too much television is bad for children.

a) Look at the yellow highlighter, these words and phrases describe the nouns. Now find and highlight three more words used to describe nouns.

b) Mark these statements as True (T) or False (F).

The descriptions in the sentences above are effective because:

i) lots of descriptive words are used. ☐

ii) the words are well-selected. ☐

iii) the words add important details. ☐

iv) long words are used. ☐

TIP ★ One 'right' word is better than a list of less suitable words. Build up your vocabulary by reading widely – newspapers, novels, articles.

8 Continue the article above by writing a paragraph about the effect of television on children's health. Highlight the descriptive phrases you have used. Would you change any of them?

TIP ★ You can learn a lot about descriptive writing from reading widely.

9 Read this extract from a story about pirates. The narrator and her sister, Minerva, are members of a pirate gang. The girls are about to take part in their first attack.

The writer uses these methods to add details.

	combination of adjectives		single adjectives
	noun phrases		simile

You never forget the first attack. I was cotton mouthed and terrified, standing at the ready, waiting to hear the two ships grind and splinter together. The waiting is the worst of it. I've seen strong men turn pale as putty and vomit over the side.
No one makes any comment. No one mocks or jeers at them, even these men who seem to laugh in the face of death itself. They stare straight ahead, gripping weapons and grappling hooks, half pikes, axes and hatchets. Sometimes, Broom ordered drums and cymbals to add to the clamour, or the cannons fired, filling the air with the reek of powder, so we boarded through blinding billows of smoke. Once on the prize, then it was different. Our own fear did not compare with the terror we instilled in the ordinary crew and passengers. We would board with reckless boldness, and if the prize offered resistance, it was kill or be killed.

As you can see, techniques are used more than once, but the writer varies the language she uses.

Highlight examples of different kinds of descriptive writing in the next paragraph.

I stood with Minerva as our first fight came, pistols primed and slung about me, my cutlass honed sharp as a razor, my axe hanging heavy from a loop on my belt.
I could not keep my legs from shaking, and my knuckles were white from gripping the rail, but Minerva had a stillness about her; her features remained calm and expressionless as if they had been carved from ironwood. It was not resignation, more a refusal to show any reaction to whatever fate was about to enfold her. I was green and sick with nervousness. She put her hand on mine to steady me, whispering though the cannon's roar.

'We will watch out for each other. We will not be afraid.'

We leaped the gap between the ships together, ready to fight and die for each other.

Adapted from *Pirates* by Celia Rees, Bloomsbury

TIP ★ It does not matter if you do not name the different kinds of words. The important thing is that you recognise how they are used. You will then be able to build them into your own writing.

Adding detail with adverbial phrases

Level 5 writers use a wider range of adverbs and some adverbial phrases.
Level 6 writers can use adverbial phrases to add detail.

This story is about a boy who has run away from home. In this section, he is caught stealing a packet of sandwiches from a shop.

When Ivan rushed into the shop, he saw the reason for all the shouting. His wife was struggling with a young boy who was fighting to get out of the door. Ivan didn't pause to think and he ran over, grabbed the boy's arm and twisted it behind his back.

This story needs more pace and drama. Re-draft to…

Ivan immediately saw the reason for all the shouting. His wife was struggling with a young boy who was savagely fighting to get out of the door. Ivan ran over and swiftly grabbed the boy's arm and twisted it behind his back.

This writing would achieve Level 5.

1 Read the next paragraph of the story. Put the adverbs beside it into different places in the sentences, e.g. before the verb, after the verb, to start the sentence.

His wife explained what had happened. The boy had grabbed a packet of sandwiches, stuffed them under his jacket and tried to run off without paying. Ivan realised the boy was crying and let go of his arm but he stood in the doorway to stop any escape.

breathlessly
suddenly
firmly
quietly

TIP ★ Practising with lots of adverbs is a good exercise but using too many adverbs is not good for your style.

Detail can be added with 'adverbial phrases'. These are groups of words that describe the verb, e.g.:

verb → adverbial phrase

The young boy was fighting with all his might to get out of the door.

2 Adverbial phrases can be added to the verb using 'with'. Add the phrases in the box to the story.

'You realise I'm going to have to call the police about this?' The boy stopped crying a) ______ but didn't say anything. 'Maria, get on the phone, will you?' His wife went behind the counter, got out her mobile and keyed in the emergency call. Ivan looked closely at the boy and realised b) ______ he knew him. 'Hang on a minute, Maria. I think I know this lad.'

He'd seen the boy before, but where? His local church ... that was it! He'd seen this lad singing in the church choir, yet here he was shoplifting. He squatted down and looked the boy in the eyes, and he said, 'What's all this about, then?' The boy looked back at him c) ______ .

with a quick wipe of his eyes	with a defiant glare	with surprise

TIP
★ Use these phrases with care.
The best thing for your writing is variety.

3 Use these writer's notes to complete the final paragraph of this story.
Write about ten sentences. Include adverbs and adverbial phrases.

Grabs mobile off Ivan's wife
Stamps on it
Pushes over one of the display stands
Dodges round Ivan
Out into the street
Too quick for Ivan to catch
Ivan stands panting at street corner
Watches helplessly as boy disappears in the park across the main road

Level 6 writers can use adverbial phrases to add detail.
Level 7 writers can use adverbial phrases to add precise detail to their writing.

Simple adverbs – e.g. *slowly, fearfully* – are easy to spot and to use.
Adverbial phrases – e.g. *with great hope* – are used to add more information about how an action happens.

4 a) You are probably used to adding adverbs to a sentence to establish a meaning. Underline the adverbs in sentences A–C.

A I shuffled hesitantly towards the door and pressed the bell.
B The girl reluctantly looked at the picture then nodded sadly.
C I made my way confidently to the exam room and quickly found my place.

Adverbial phrases can be used to add a little more detail.

★ I shuffled with nervous hesitation towards the door and pressed the bell.
★ The girl reluctantly looked at the picture then nodded with sad recognition.

A different effect can be created placing the adverb or adverbial at the start of a sentence. Compare these two sentences:

I turned fearfully around. ⇒ With fear and dread, I turned slowly around.

b) Change these sentences to place emphasis on the adverbial.

i) The dancer leapt confidently onto the stage to rapturous applause.

With ______________________________

____

ii) Josh plunged desperately back into the sea to save the dog from the crushing waves.

In ______________________________

____

iii) Hannah smiled shyly but hopefully as she was called up to accept the award.

____

____

5 Practise placing an adverbial at the start to focus a reader. Highlight just **two** sentences you decide to improve. Write them out and don't forget the comma!

★ Don't over use the idea or it becomes repetitive.

The atmosphere in the stadium was tense. The crowd grimly waited for the match to start. Their team had gained promotion easily last season, but this season had been a different story. They had played capably but lacked the quality needed to survive at this level. The ref blew for kick-off. Thousands of faces looked on anxiously from the terraces.

6 This paragraph has too many dull, short sentences. Give it more impact by combining some sentences in the ways described above. Copy out your new version.

My heart was beating frantically. I tried to control the car. I knew that the brakes had failed. I wasn't too pleased to be on the steepest road in Europe. I concentrated as hard as I could and kept a firm grip on the steering wheel. A tight bend was approaching. I knew I couldn't hold the car on the road. There was only one thing that might save my life. I could crash into the sheer rock face on my left. I prayed to whatever god was looking down on me and swung the wheel to the left.

Another way to use adverbials to create more effective writing is to combine two sentences into one:

adverb

I crept quietly into the room. I saw what was going on.

adverb

When I crept quietly into the room, I saw what was going on.

adverbial phrase

Creeping into the room with silent steps, I saw what was going on.

The first version of this sentence is a bit flat. The second version is fine. The third version has a slightly stronger impact.

TIP ★ Do not overuse this technique. Use it to vary your writing.

Using a full range of punctuation

Level 5 writers use a wider range of punctuation accurately.
Level 6 writers use a full range of punctuation accurately.

1 Tick all the punctuation items you are confident with. Practise those you are not so happy about.

Checklist

Full stops: ☐ *I'm sure I don't need to explain these.*

Commas for clauses: ☐ *Although you are good at punctuation, a little revision always helps.*

Commas as brackets: ☐ *A lot of people, myself included, make some slips of punctuation.*

Full punctuation of speech: ☐ *My old teacher used to say, 'Punctuation keeps the train of your ideas on track.'*

Semi-colons: ☐ *It's great to remember my old school; I had a wonderful time there.*

2 Punctuate this paragraph using the following punctuation:

- commas;
- full stops;
- a question mark;
- speech marks;
- one semi-colon.

The interview had been arranged for 10 o'clock and I arrived at reception 10 minutes early I wanted to make a good impression my father who had been in the army for 20 years had drummed into me the importance of being on time On time means you're on the ball he used to say to me it was a lesson I had never forgotten it served me well that day if I hadn't have been early I wouldn't have seen the man who staggered out of the lift he was holding a blood-stained handkerchief to his face and looked as if he was about to faint a strange thought crossed my mind was he on the interview list before me I offered to help him but he left the building muttering no job's worth that when I looked at my watch I saw my turn had come

Revising semi-colons

Use a semi-colon (;) when you want to show a connection between two sentences, e.g. when the second sentence depends on what is described in the first sentence.

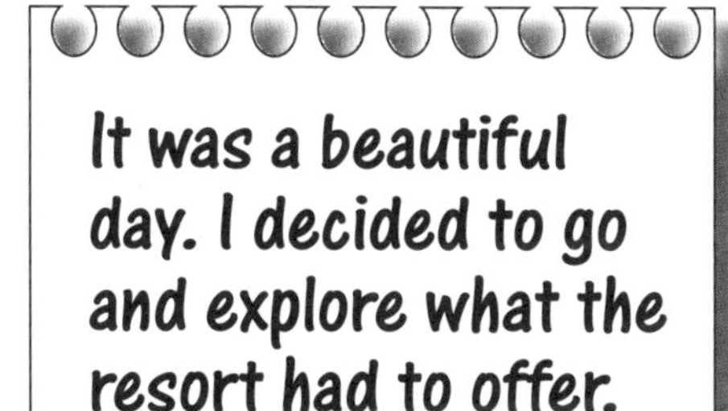

It was a beautiful day; I decided to go and explore what the resort had to offer.

If you want to show the reader you decided to explore the resort because it was a beautiful day, use a semi-colon.

★ Use semi-colons carefully. They lose their effect if you use too many.

3 Highlight two sentences in each example that you think could be joined by a semi-colon.

A

It was Saturday so I woke later than usual. My mum was clattering around the kitchen and Dad was out playing golf. My sister had gone shopping. Saturday belonged to me. I could do just what I wanted. Well, that's what I thought.

B

The car ate up the miles of empty road. John looked around at the strange landscape and he thought back to how this journey had all started. It all began one year ago. In those 12 months he had changed so much. His thoughts were interrupted by the wail of a police siren.

4 a) Punctuate the paragraph below, then write out your version. Use these guidelines:

- ★ change most commas to full stops;
- ★ change one comma to a semi-colon;
- ★ keep one comma.

The waiting crowd suddenly lost patience, I was caught up in the rush of people and carried along, bounced this way and that, I was like a cork in a rushing stream, suddenly a shot rang out and the crowd stumbled to a stop, a soldier was on the bridge and he was holding a rifle, it was pointed straight at the crowd, some sort of control had at last been established.

There is more than one answer, but you are now at a level where you can choose the effect you want.

b) Now write out a differently punctuated version. What is the difference you have created?

Level 6 writers use a full range of punctuation accurately.
Level 7 writers use punctuation to make meaning clear, and for effect.

Practise using punctuation accurately to make meaning clear.

5 Punctuation can change the meanings in sentences, as the example shows. Write out sentences A–C twice each using punctuation to create different meanings.

Example

Slow animals on the road

Slow! Animals on the road.

Tells someone to go more slowly because there are animals on the road.

Slow animals on the road.

Tells us the animals are moving slowly.

A Go get Dad help.

____

____

B Sarah said Amy is bossy.

____

____

C After I left Dave Andy and Sam went to a party.

____

____

6 a) Build the words and phrases below into a sentence using five commas and a full stop.

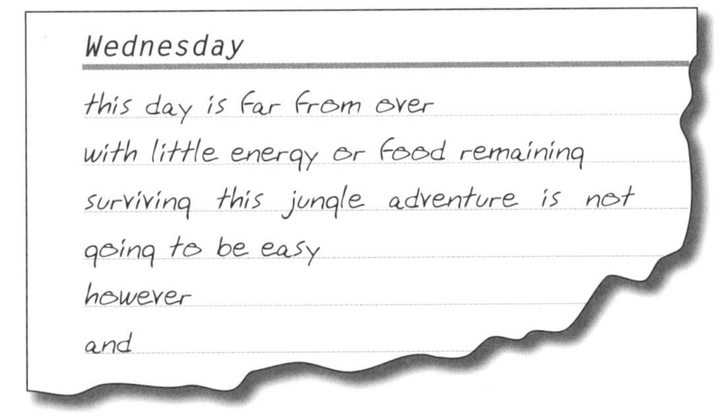

For example, you could begin:
Surviving this jungle adventure … or
This day is far from over … or
With little energy …

b) Then build the sentence again, changing the word order (use the same punctuation).

Punctuation can be used to add emphasis to particular points in a sentence.

7 Consider the difference between these two sentences:

A *Sam waited as patiently as she could for the plane to get her out of the jungle.*

B *Sam waited, as patiently as she could, for the plane to get her out of the jungle.*

a) Which sentence (A or B) suggests that Sam is finding it difficult to be patient?

As you can see, the commas draw attention to the phrase they contain. This gives you, as a writer, the power to choose to emphasise certain phrases in your writing.

b) Create sentences to continue this story. Write one sentence for each picture. Practise using commas to emphasise parts of your sentences.

TIP ★ Do not use this effect too often or your writing will sound silly!

Improve the organisation of your writing

Level 5 writers give openings and closings to their work.
Level 6 writers give clear openings and closings, and make links between sections.

Readers need signposts to help them through a piece of writing. This helps them to understand and agree with, or get involved in, your writing.

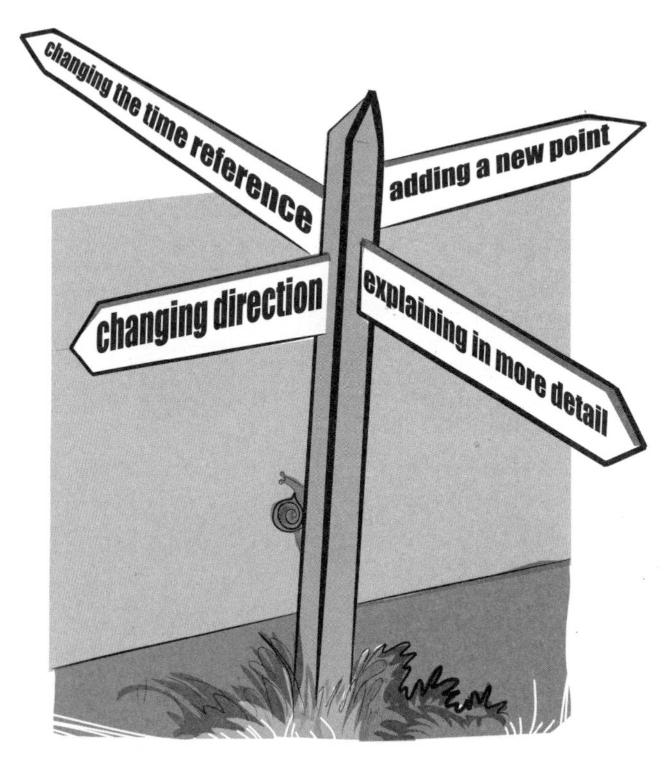

1 Words that work as signposts are helpful to a writer and reader.
Add these words to the table below:

- ★ finally
- ★ next
- ★ first
- ★ however
- ★ eventually
- ★ despite this
- ★ in contrast
- ★ soon
- ★ afterwards
- ★ meanwhile
- ★ in addition
- ★ after this

Words that give order to instructions	Words that show time in a story	Words that link ideas in an argument

Linking words and phrases prepare readers for the direction you will take them in.
Practise using linking sections in the tasks below.

2 Continue this story in two different ways, using the handwritten words to begin the next paragraph.

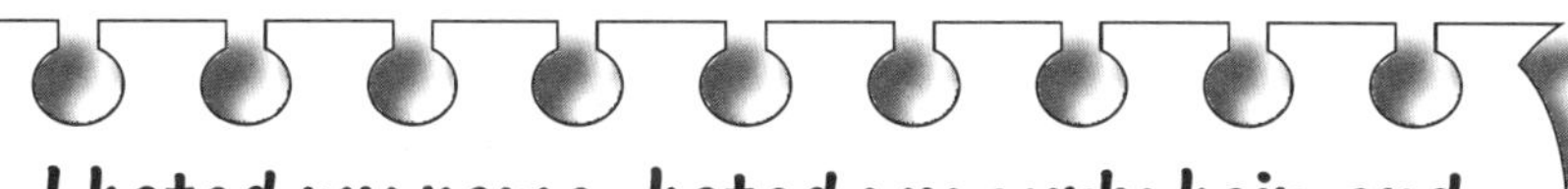

I hated my name, hated my curly hair, and especially hated the shape of my ears.

In contrast, ... **Eventually, ...**

---

3 Continue this news article in three different ways using the linking words below.

The fairy tale goes like this: they are high-school sweethearts from a small town. He graduates from high school, becomes a soldier and goes to war.

Despite this, ... **However, ...** **As soon as ...**

TIP

★ Not all links have to be made using these words. Sometimes the content of the sections makes a clear link.

Level 6 writers can use paragraphs to sequence and control ideas and information.
Level 7 writers can use different styles of paragraph to add interest and impact to their writing.

4 What effects can you achieve with these paragraph styles?

Draw a line to link the paragraph type with one or more effects.

Paragraph type	Effect
single-sentence paragraphs	for dramatic effect
long paragraphs	to build up logical ideas or tension
paragraphs with a change of direction in the middle	to surprise a reader
repeated short paragraphs throughout the writing	to echo a point throughout the writing
paragraphs that begin and end with the same sentence	to emphasise a point
repeated pattern of paragraph openings, e.g. one word sentences	to interest the reader

TIP
★ Practise using different paragraph styles in your everyday writing.

5 Read this article, which aims to persuade the reader to take action about global warming. The article tries to persuade people to make changes to their lifestyles to reduce harm to the environment. The content is good, but the presentation is rather dull.

SIMPLE STEPS TO SAVE OUR PLANET

You don't have to go miles away from home to protest, or spend masses of money. If you try to follow the few simple steps that I shall now give you, you will have started to help us all. First, plant a tree. This could be easier than it sounds. Join or help out a local wildlife group and ask to plant a tree. Trees, when fully grown, will help keep the planet cooler. On the same point, you could protest against the demolition of the rainforests. This is the same principle, we need the trees to cool our planet and yet they are chopping them down to create roads or buildings. Something as simple as walking instead of taking the car will help reduce pollution. As well as stopping pollution, you are giving yourself exercise, something important for our bodies. So the next time you get into your car, or your motorbike, think – do I have to make this journey by vehicle or can I walk? When you are at home, and you're getting a little cold, put a jumper on and do not adjust the heating. The extra heat produced by our homes also affects the planet. So try wearing an extra layer in winter.

a) Rewrite the article, varying paragraph styles to add interest and impact. Use the ideas on the previous page to help you.

b) Highlight examples of the different paragraph styles you have used in your writing and label them with the descriptions from page 26.

c) Create a **mnemonic** to help you remember the variety of different paragraph styles.

Definition

A mnemonic is a word made up of the starting letter of words you want to remember, e.g. KIS – keep it simple.

TIP

★ Practise making yourself use different paragraph styles.

Improve your informative writing 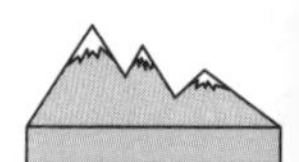

Level 5 writers choose language to inform and interest the reader.
Level 6 writers use language confidently to convince the reader.

1 Imagine your headteacher has decided to change the existing school uniform and replace it with a more traditional style of blazer, with smart trousers for the boys and straight skirts for the girls. Read this item in your school newsletter, which the head has written to explain the decision.

New Street High School

Introduces subject matter in a formal tone.

After careful thought and close consultation with parents, I have decided to make a change to the existing school uniform.

Also claims he has a lot of support.

Topic is old uniform. Adds detail to explanation to make a more convincing case.

I, and many others, felt that the existing uniform was in need of a radical overhaul. The blue sweatshirt and grey trousers did not seem to fit in with the new image of the school that we all wish to promote. Too often, the sweatshirt became a grubby, sloppy-looking item of clothing. Many pupils have suggested that they felt the sweatshirt was too informal and better suited to the gym rather than the classroom. The trousers were not popular with many of the girls.

Moves to new topic – the new uniform. Piles up positive vocabulary to promote the idea.

The new uniform will create a more mature and business-like atmosphere. It has been designed by a leading fashion expert and is intended to suggest the type of clothes worn by successful men and women of the world of work. Several pupils have tried on the designs and assured me that they felt both comfortable and smart in them.

Moves to topic of what is going to happen next.

I will be sending to all parents/guardians a leaflet that contains photographs of the new uniform, as well as a list of prices and suppliers. This should be with you by the end of term.

Strong conclusion.

I know you will support the school in this new, and exciting, venture.

You might, or might not, agree with the views of the head, but the explanation is clear and strong.

2 Find examples of these features in the head's explanation and highlight them in the text.

- Clear introduction.
- Clear paragraph structure with topic sentences.
- Careful use of details and vocabulary to support point of view.
- Adopts a formal tone to suggest authority.
- Strong conclusion.

3 Choose **one** of the following topics and explain your views in an article for the school newsletter. Write your explanation following the model of the teacher on page 28.

Topics

- Remove all soft-drinks vending machines from a school site.
- Boys and girls should be educated in separate schools.
- Pupils should be able to leave school at 15 years of age.

Level 6 writers select ideas to inform the reader.
Level 7 writers select language and ideas to interest and inform the reader.

Level 7 writers make many choices before they begin writing. Think about the following things.

Form of the writing

- What to include – which are the best details to do the job?
- Style required – newspaper report, historical account, biography, etc. and the features of this style.

How to address the reader

- Formal or informal language?
- Economical and direct or more elaborate use of language?

4 Read this newspaper article, then answer the questions on page 31.

Shoe that grows with your child

This clever little invention could be the answer for every parent who spends a fortune on children's shoes. It's an extending shoe – which grows with your children's feet. The trainer – touted as the next big thing – has just reached our shores from America.

Parents simply press a button on the side and gently pull to fit. Hey presto, the size 10 trainer suddenly becomes a size 11. Each pair covers one full size, in half-size increments. So a size 10 can be extended to a size 10½, then again to an 11.

And a number on the heel tells parents which size they've lengthened them to.

The Inchworm trainer comes in three models and a variety of colours and costs around £48.

'These are a great idea,' said Theresa Gree, 32, from Southampton, Hants, who bought a pair for her seven-year-old daughter, Phoebe.

She said: 'Phoebe's feet are growing so quickly. Now, rather than having to go shopping every time, I can make the shoe bigger.'

The trainers use 'iFit' technology, which means they are easy to adjust but sturdy enough not to change size accidentally. The makers say they will stand up to the most boisterous use.

Brand manager Peter Craig, of Scottish distributors Fat Shoes Day, said: 'My son-in-law went to America and came back very excited about Inchworm shoes.

'They are a fantastic idea that could make parents' lives a whole lot easier.

'They are also great for the thousands of kids who have one foot bigger than the other – they could have one shoe set at size 11 and one at 11½.'

He added: 'We have sold more than 500 pairs in the UK already.'

a) The article contains different kinds of well-selected information to inform and interest the reader. Highlight these different kinds of information in the article and label them.

b) Notice that the writer chooses comments from people (reported speech) for two different purposes:

i) to introduce new information;

ii) to offer opinion.

Identify these different purposes of speech in the article.

c) The tone of the article is quite neutral – it is neither very formal nor informal. However, the words are well chosen and precise for the job they need to do (e.g. the language to describe the shoe is precise). Match the language in the first column below with the Level 7 language used in the article (second column).

Meaning	Language in article
different styles of trainers	half-size increments
made bigger	extended
strong	variety of models
make them different sizes	sturdy
heavy wear and tear	the most boisterous use

TIP

★ Include a variety of precise vocabulary in your writing to interest your reader.

Improve your persuasive writing

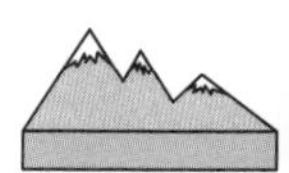

Level 5 writers use some techniques to influence a reader.
Level 6 writers can produce persuasive writing using a variety of techniques.

Persuasive techniques help to get your audience's attention and convince them of your ideas.

1 Read this speech by Martin Luther King, a civil rights activist campaigning for racial equality in the USA in the 1960s.

There are many techniques here that Level 6 writers can adopt.

> I have a dream that one day this nation will rise up and live out the true meaning of its creed: 'We hold these truths to be self-evident, that all men are created equal.'
>
> I have a dream that one day on the red hills of Georgia, the sons of former slaves and the sons of former slave owners will be able to sit down together at the table of brotherhood.
>
> I have a dream that one day even the state of Mississippi, a state sweltering with the heat of injustice, sweltering with the heat of oppression, will be transformed into an oasis of freedom and justice.
>
> I have a dream that my four little children will one day live in a nation where they will not be judged by the colour of their skin but by the content of their character.
>
> I have a *dream* today!

a) Label the highlighted text with the techniques in the left-hand column.

TECHNIQUES	REASON
using a quotation	to make your idea seem real or familiar to people
giving a positive idea	to build an impression in your audience's mind
repeating a phrase	so that people will remember your idea
giving a personal example	to show that things are not good now
giving a negative example	to give authority to your idea
finishing with a short, dramatic point	to show your idea will be good

b) Match the techniques with the reason why they have been used.
One has been done for you.

2 Make a list, in your own words, of techniques to use in a persuasive speech.

Emotive language

Language that appeals to the emotions of your reader works well in persuasive writing. It is known as **emotive language**.

3 Imagine pupils at your school have voted to get rid of school uniform. Your job is to convince parents and teachers it's a good idea.

a) Read this speech from someone who wants to keep school uniform. Identify the persuasive techniques that have been used by using the boxes and drawing lines to examples in the text. Use your own list and the techniques on page 32.

Uniform offers a sense of identity. The army, the police and the health service all use uniforms to give their members the sense that they belong to an organisation. School uniform is like this too; it gives everyone an equal opportunity to show they are a part of the community of the school. It also presents an identifiable sign to the general public that we are proud to belong to the school.

Uniform offers equality. After the initial expense of buying a uniform, parents do not have to worry about buying the latest brand name clothes so that their children will 'fit in'. Uniform is what it says: the same for everyone.

Uniform makes life easy. It removes the need to make difficult decisions about 'what to wear' each morning. I know, from experience, that having to think about breakfast is enough in the mornings – let alone what colour socks to wear!

Basically, uniform works for schools. Don't undo the good work.

b) Prepare a speech to persuade parents and teachers that non-uniform is the right way to go. Use as many persuasive techniques as you can.

c) Check your work to identify the techniques you have used.

d) Think about a redraft. How would you improve the speech?

Level 6 writers can produce persuasive writing using a variety of techniques.

Level 7 writers can persuade a reader by choosing information with care and presenting it with passion and style.

4 Read this text by Malcolm X, who campaigned for Civil Rights in America during the 1950s and 60s. Here he argues against the 'sit-in' form of protest.

Students all over the world today are standing up for their rights and fighting for their rights, but here in America, the so-called Negro students have allowed themselves to be manoeuvered under a tag of 'sit-in'. The word 'sit' itself is not an honorable tag; anybody can sit, an old woman can sit, a coward can sit, a baby can sit, anything can sit, but it takes a man to stand ... Rather than to force our way into someone else's restaurant or public place that they have established, we should get our own. Once we have our own, we're respected for the fact that we can create our own. That's equality right there.

Revise your persuasive writing skills by identifying these features of Malcolm X's style:

a) repetition
b) examples
c) contrast
d) short, dramatic sentence

Match the feature to the highlighted text.

5 How you open a persuasive piece of writing will depend on your reader, or listener. Read this speech by Hilary Clinton, an American politician. She is addressing the United Nations Conference on Women, arguing that people still need to work for the equality for women in all parts of the world.

This is truly a celebration – a celebration of the contributions women make in every aspect of life: in the home, on the job, in their communities, as mothers, wives, sisters, daughters, learners, workers, citizens and leaders.

Fill the gaps with the words below.

Hilary Clinton describes the conference as a celebration at the a) ______ of the speech. Creating a b) ______ feeling at the start can help to persuade the reader to 'co-operate' with your c) ______. The d) ______ technique of shocking your reader creates a different, powerful opening. Think about your reader and e) ______ the right opening.

opposite	start	shocking	positive	choose	point of view

6 Continue to read Hilary Clinton's speech, then complete the tasks below.

We come together in fields and in factories. In village markets and supermarkets. In living rooms and board rooms.

Whether it is while playing with our children in the park, or washing clothes in a river, or taking a break at the office water cooler, we come together and talk about our aspirations and concerns. And time and again, our talk turns to our children and our families.
However different we may be, there is far more that unites us than divides us. We share a common future. And we are here to find common ground so that we may help bring new dignity and respect to women and girls all over the world – and in so doing, bring new strength and stability to families as well.

a) Which colour highlighter is used for:

i) familiar examples based in ordinary life?

ii) examples of **abstract ideas**?

Definition

An abstract idea is a 'big' idea such as 'imagination, weakness, triumph'.

b) Why has the writer mixed these two types of examples?

7 Write a positive opening to a persuasive speech to your local council about the lack of facilities for young people in your area. Then write an opening intended to shock.

Using a variety of techniques keeps a reader, or listener, interested but you also have to lead them clearly through your ideas.

TIP

★ Use information or examples with which your reader is familiar to get them on your side. You can then introduce more complicated or more powerful points to make them think.

8 Write two paragraphs of a letter to persuade people to donate money to a children's charity. Use familiar examples and abstract ideas.

Improve your imaginative writing

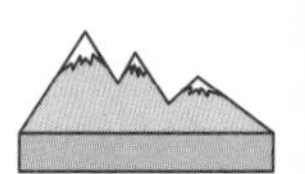

Level 5 writers tell a story, making careful decisions about character and action.
Level 6 writers build atmosphere and character in stories with careful choice of words.

1 Read texts A and B, which both respond to the task: *Write a story about discovering an object that reminds you of your past*. The pieces are roughly the same length, but they achieve different effects.

A

The further I went up, the darker it was getting. Soon the darkness of the room was dazzling and there was only the light of my mobile phone to keep me from not getting lost or tripping over an object and injuring myself.

There it was – the attic door. I cautiously opened the door. I was almost frightened. I hadn't been up there for years. Every visible object was smothered in a thick coat of dust and fly-infested cobwebs.

B

I asked mum where it was and she said that it might still be in the loft. I asked her if I could go up and have a look and she said I could so I got the ladder, which was getting old. The steps creaked and it looked very wobbly. I lifted the loft lid and stepped inside. The blackness was blinding. I felt around trying to find the light cord. Yes, I found it, pulled it and a very dull bulb came on.

One of the texts above is Level 5 and one is Level 6.

a) Which do you think is Level 6?

b) How do you know?

2 a) Which features of story writing does the highlighter on page 36 identify? One has been done for you.

Features of story writing

★ Carefully choosing words to create atmosphere.	
★ Using phrases that help to control pace (speed).	
★ Using uninteresting background detail.	
★ Showing off language skills through interesting images.	blue

b) Tick the features that are good to use.

c) Which of these language areas do you most need to improve?

TIP ★ A main difference between Level 5 and Level 6 is often the care with which details and words are chosen. Taking out words and sentences that are not interesting can help a piece of writing.

3 Rewrite the section on page 36 highlighted in grey. It is not a very interesting part of the story, so just keep it short.

4 a) Continue text A to the point where the person discovers what they are looking for.

TIP ★ Use as much interesting language as you can – show off!

b) Review your work using the highlighters to identify:

★ precise words used for description;
★ phrases that control pace;
★ 'show-off' style images (like 'dazzled by darkness').

c) Write a list of useful techniques for story writing.

Level 6 writers build atmosphere and character in stories with careful choice of words.
Level 7 writers can 'show' character and atmosphere through details within the plot.

Introducing character or mood

5 Read this text, which **tells** the reader about a character in quite an obvious way.

I have a client named Teddy Franklin. Teddy Franklin is a car thief. He is 32 years old and he is one of the best car thieves on the Eastern seaboard. Cadillac Ted is so good that he is able to support himself as a car thief. He has been arrested repeatedly, which is how he made my acquaintance, but he has never done time*. That is because I am so good. It is also because Teddy is so good.

* *done time – been in prison*

Kennedy for the Defense: A Novel by George V. Higgins

a) Highlight any information you can find about Teddy. One example has been done for you.

b) A different way to introduce characters into your writing is to **show** the reader what the character is like, rather than **tell** them. Continue this alternative character description, adding any extra information you would like to, to show Teddy's character while he is stealing a car.

Strolling down the quiet side-street, Teddy Franklin was moderately attractive, but not handsome enough to turn heads …

c) Read your own work and highlight the ways you show Teddy's character.

TIP ★ Using interesting words helps your reader – and gets you good marks!

A writer can **tell** a reader about the setting of a story, or **show** them. The effect on the reader is like the difference between looking at a photograph or watching video.

★ **Telling** or **showing** can be the right choice for different kinds of stories.

Telling

This description is from a famous novel. The writer has chosen to **tell** the reader about the setting.

> A few miles south of Soledad, the Salinas River drops in close to the hill-side bank and runs deep and green. The water is warm too, for it has slipped twinkling over the yellow sands in the sunlight before reaching the narrow pool.
>
> *Of Mice and Men* by John Steinbeck

Showing

This description **shows** the landscape through a character's viewpoint.

> Mikey stood on the hill gazing proudly over the landscape before him; the hillsides falling to the valley floor where the clear, cool stream flowed brightly down towards the sea. This was his home. And he was glad to be back.

6 A writer can choose whether to show or tell about the setting. Think about the reasons for choosing each technique. Draw lines to show the effects of telling and showing a setting.

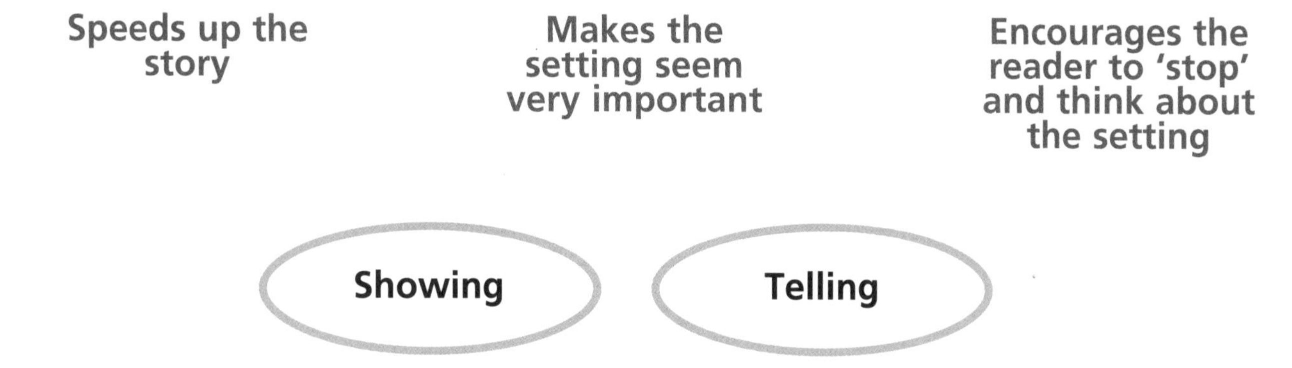

7 Practise writing your own **show** or **tell** settings for these stories.
Write one paragraph for each.

- ★ A stormy scene in a ghost story.
- ★ A jungle setting for an adventure story.
- ★ A kitchen scene for a 'teenage life' story.
- ★ An aeroplane setting for a hijack story.

Improve your writing to review

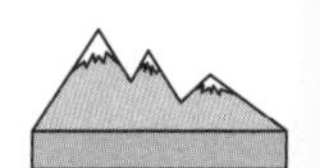

Level 5 writers explain opinions clearly and politely.
Level 6 writers explain opinions in detail, using an appropriate tone.

1 Imagine this report has appeared in your local newspaper. Read it carefully.

Election vote winner?

Voters will be making their minds up at next month's local elections. The Independent Party candidate, Mary Forest, hopes she has a vote winner with her idea of 'Teenage Service'.

What it involves

She plans to send squads of young people to clear up litter, clean ponds, create nature areas and help to install new playground equipment. She also thinks many pensioners would welcome some help to clear up their gardens.

Summer projects

She proposes that all 13–18-year-olds should spend two weeks of every summer term involved in various projects to improve the local environment and community. She believes that both teenagers and the community would benefit from her idea.

Send us your views

This newspaper would like to gather local feeling on the proposal. We invite you to set out your views. Send them to us and the most interesting contribution will appear in next week's edition of this paper.

The newspaper editor is looking at some comments. Tick the two that would be suitable to appear in the paper.

- ★ I'm not giving up my time. Mary Forest is obviously mad … ☐
- ★ I'm not old enough to vote but I'm old enough to have my say about … ☐
- ★ I already help my gran out, so that's it as far as I'm … ☐
- ★ I wonder if Mary Forest has actually asked teenagers what they think about … ☐
- ★ She should be locked up … ☐

TIP
★ A quick plan makes sure you include the most important points.
Then, when you are writing, you can focus on your language.

2 Now set out your view on Mary Forest's proposals. Make sure your readers can follow your ideas.

TIP
★ Remember why you're writing and that your comments could appear in public. You need to show you are giving serious thought to the issue.

The opening sentences of your paragraphs can be helpful signposts. They don't have to be boring. You might want to make your reader sit up and take notice.

> If Mrs Forest asked for volunteers instead of ordering us around, she might be surprised at how many of us are interested in improving the environment …

> Putting up playground equipment is a skilled job, not one for a bunch of amateurs. If I were a parent, I'd want to know my kids were safe …

Next, try to create interesting starts for paragraphs about any three of these topics.

★ Litter clearing
★ Tidying pensioners' gardens
★ Pond cleaning
★ What would happen if pupils refused to turn up
★ Not having enough time for school exams

To present your views convincingly, you'll need to build up your sentences. Use connectives in the middle or at the start of sentences to help, e.g.:

I agree with your wish to improve the community. You are going about it in the wrong way.

Becomes

I agree with your wish to improve the community although you are going about it in the wrong way.

Or

Although I agree with your wish to improve the community, you are going about it in the wrong way.

______________________ ______________________ ______________________

______________________ ______________________ ______________________

______________________ ______________________ ______________________

______________________ ______________________ ______________________

TIP
★ Remember: there are many useful connectives, e.g. *if, as, because, until, when, except, since, where, even if, however, on the other hand*. Try to use some when you write your response.

Level 6 writers explain opinions precisely.

Level 7 writers interestingly explain precise opinions.

You need to make sure that you can interest your reader, not just by your ideas but also by the way you express them. You need to:

- ★ command the attention of your reader;
- ★ keep them interested;
- ★ leave them with a strong final impression.

People applying for a job on a teenage magazine have been asked to write a favourable review of a film called *White Heat*. The person who shows the most promising writing skills will get called for interview. Imagine your job is to look through the reviews to decide who should go forward to the interview. Here are three opening paragraphs. Choose the one you think is the best.

Reviewer 1

Your money will be well spent if you pay out to go and see *White Heat*, the latest all-action thriller featuring heart-throb cop Ben Dillon. He gets killed at the end. I didn't expect that, but that's what a surprise ending is, I suppose.

Reviewer 2

I went to see White Heat last week and it was really good. I had a really nice evening. I started out a six o'clock and didn't get home until really late. What a night!

Reviewer 3

Ben Dillon? Not my favourite actor ... but after seeing him in White Heat, I own up to being so very wrong. His performance here is perfect. If you only see one film this year, make it this one. Films just don't come any better.

I hope you rejected Reviewers 1 and 2. Perhaps Reviewer 3 still has things to learn, but the other two make serious mistakes.

Reviewer 1 was favourable and lively but spoilt the film by revealing the ending.

Reviewer 2 was favourable but boring. The vocabulary was dull and irrelevant details had been included.

Reviewer 3 catches attention with the opening comment then surprises the reader with a change in direction.

Important lessons can be learned from these reviewers.

★ Grab your reader's attention with the first sentence. Choose words that have some impact.

3 Read the following paragraphs in which the writers review a film of their choice. Then read the judge's notes to see strengths and weaknesses in the reviews.

Indicates topic but in unimaginative way.

If you go to see this film, you can expect to see an all-action thriller. It has a lot of suspense, too. You are always trying to work out what's going to happen next. If you like that sort of thing, you'll really love this film. Next, I'm going to write about the film's stars.

No variety of sentence structure and vocabulary.

No interesting details to provoke reader curiosity.

Outlines topic of plot. Goes on to give broad idea of storyline.

The story begins in modern-day New York and ends - I know this might be hard to believe - in the age of the dinosaurs. What happens between those two points is what keeps the audience intrigued from beginning to end. It all starts when a computer geek (the bespectacled Ben Dillon) hacks into secret US government files. His discovery there puts his life on the line and so begins an amazing hide-and-seek story which, as I've indicated, becomes prehistoric! On the way, he meets the delectable Polly (co-star Lisa Lane). Romance blossoms between these two stunning stars.

Directly addresses reader to help create lively, friendly tone.

Includes details to make things more memorable for the reader.

Provides a link into next topic – the stars' performance.

4 Now show what you have learned. Write a film or TV programme review for the magazine. It can be imaginary or based on something you have seen.

Writing self-assessment sheets

★ Look at the descriptions in the Level 6 section of the table.

★ In your work, find examples of the descriptions in the table.

★ Highlight the description in the table and an example in your work.

★ If you have at least ten of the Level 6 descriptions highlighted, you have achieved Level 6.

★ In a different colour, highlight what you still need to improve.

Level	Sentence structure	Punctuation	Paragraph organisation	Organisation inside paragraphs	Effect on the reader
6	I am beginning to choose my language for its effect on the reader, eg.: I use longer sentences when I want to show relationships between ideas; I use short sentences for emphasis or drama when needed; I use different types of words to open sentences, e.g. ___ing words, ___ly words, time (*Five days later* ...).	Most of my punctuation is correct. I can use commas, instead of brackets, for 'extra' information in sentences. I can sometimes use semi-colons correctly when they are required.	I can use paragraphs of different lengths to help my reader, or to create an effect. My opening paragraph clearly introduces ideas that I will follow up later in the writing. I use a range of connecting words to link my paragraphs, e.g. *Consequently ..., Soon after this ..., In addition ...* etc.	My paragraphs have a clear theme, which is developed across a number of sentences. Sometimes I delay giving information to my reader to create a better effect. I give my reader clear signals about the direction of the writing, e.g. *In the end ... In contrast ... Overall ...*, etc.	I write in a style that suits the format of a story or a description. I help my reader to get involved in my writing by using interesting and precise details. I try to use some ambitious language to interest my reader, e.g. *dazzling darkness, perfect candidate.*
5	I use a range of different sentence types. I use different openings for my sentences, e.g. *I think ...The train stopped ... If ...* I use connectives such as *although, while* and *even if* to link ideas in my sentences. I can use some 'strings of verbs' accurately, e.g. *I will be able to visit ... He could have jumped ...*	The ends of my sentences are correctly punctuated. When I use speech punctuation, I place the commas correctly. I use commas to mark clauses for sentences beginning with *Although ..., Because ..., If ..., When ...*, etc.	The order of my paragraphs is logical, e.g. most important to least important points/clear time sequence. My conclusion has links to my introduction or the main idea of the text, e.g. by summarising in an argument or tying up loose ends in a story.	My paragraphs have a main point and a number of 'smaller points' on the same topic. My paragraphs openings give clear signals to the reader, e.g. a topic sentence or *Later*, etc.	I develop my ideas across a number of sentences. I use a range of interesting words that make my ideas clear, e.g. *worthwhile, recommend, suitable.* I recognise my reader by using words that suit the task, e.g. *to be polite, to persuade.*

★ Look at the Level 7 descriptions in the table. In your work, find examples of the descriptions in the table. Highlight the description in the table and an example in your work.

★ If you have at least ten of the Level 7 descriptions highlighted, you have achieved Level 7.

★ In a different colour, highlight what you still need to improve.

Level	Sentence structure	Punctuation	Paragraph organisation	Organisation inside paragraphs	Effect on the reader
7	I choose my language carefully, thinking about how it will affect the reader and how it suits the type of text I am writing. I use a range of different sentence types such as: embedded clauses, e.g. *Kamal, who is famed for his outrageous practical jokes, had gone too far this time*; repetition, e.g. *Sara was in trouble – more trouble than she had ever imagined*; balanced phrases, e.g. *Love can open up a new world, or close everything down.* I use a wide range of sentence openings such as those above in Level 6 and: Inversion, e.g. *Had I known …, Never did I …,* etc. I can use a wide range of connectives such as *despite, whenever, as a consequence of.* I write concisely, e.g. I don't use ten words when six words will do the job.	I use a range of punctuation to make my writing clear. I can use punctuation to have a particular effect on my reader. I can use commas to separate a whole clause in a sentence (see **embedded clauses**). I can sometimes use a dash to add an idea. I can use brackets to separate ideas for my reader, or to make a comment.	There is an overall plan to my writing. Events in a story or points in an argument are all part of a larger overview. I can affect the reader's response to my writing by controlling the way I give information, e.g. hiding some character details, presenting an argument against my point then disproving it. I sometimes link my paragraphs with key words (as in Level 6) **but** I can also make clear links from one paragraph to another through the content and ideas without using connecting words.	My paragraphs are carefully constructed to affect the reader, e.g.: short (even one-word) paragraphs to shock or emphasise; longer paragraphs holding together a complex argument; paragraphs with repeated patterns to interest or inform the reader. I have chosen the first and last sentences of a paragraph to link or contrast with other paragraphs.	I write with confidence and some individuality in a style that suits the format of a speech or a review. I engage my reader in my writing with precise and economic selection of details. I am adventurous with language choices to impress and influence my reader.

Pages 8–9: Using a wider range of connectives (L5–6)

1 **a)** when **b)** as **c)** before **d)** although
2 **a)** as/before/when/after **b)** although
3 **a)** When **b)** Even though
4 *Check your answer with your teacher.*

Pages 10–11: Using a wider range of connectives (L6–7)

5 **A** – yellow; **B** – blue; **C** – green; **D** – green; **E** – pink
6 *Sample answers:*
When the day of the visit finally arrived, the rest of the school went off to normal classes. At 10 o'clock, the Drama group crowded noisily outside the Hall until Miss Fox appeared and gave us one of her 'I'm waiting for quiet looks.' Although we pretended not to notice her for a minute, we gave in eventually. Silence reigned. We waited. After she had made her point, she told us to line up quietly. Finally, we were allowed in.
The day of the visit finally arrived and the rest of the school went off to normal classes. When 10 o'clock arrived, the Drama group crowded noisily outside the Hall and Miss Fox appeared. Although she gave us one of her 'I'm waiting for quiet' looks, we pretended not to notice her for a minute. However, after a session of eyeball popping, we gave in. Silence. We waited. ... and waited until she felt she had made her point. Eventually, she told us to line up quietly and we were allowed in.
7 *Check your answer with your teacher.*

Pages 12–13: Adding detail with descriptive phrases (L5–6)

1–6 *Check your answer with your teacher.*

Pages 14–15: Adding detail with descriptive phrases (L6–7)

7 **a)** *Check your answer with your teacher.*
b) i) T **ii)** T **iii)** T **iv)** F
8 *Show this to your teacher.*
9 first fight; as sharp as a razor; as calm ... ironwood; green ... with nervousness; cannon's roar

Pages 16–17: Adding detail with adverbial phrases (L5–6)

1 *Check your answer with your teacher.*
2 **a)** with a quick wipe of his eyes
b) with surprise
c) with a defiant glare
3 *Check your answer with your teacher.*

Pages 18–19: Adding detail with adverbial phrases (L6–7)

4 **a) A** hesitantly; **B** reluctantly, sadly; **C** confidently, quickly
b) i) With confidence **ii)** In desperation **iii)** With a shy but hopeful smile
5 *Sample answers:*
Grimly, the crowd waited for the match to start.
Anxiously, thousands of faces looked on from the terraces.
With mounting anxiety, thousands of faces looked on from the terraces.
6 *Check your answer with your teacher.*

Pages 20–21: Using a full range of punctuation (L5–6)

2 The interview had been arranged for 10 o'clock and I arrived at reception 10 minutes early. (;) I wanted to make a good impression. My father, who had been in the army for 20 years, had drummed into me the importance of being on time. 'On time means you're on the ball,' he used to say to me. It was a lesson I had never forgotten. (;) It served me well that day. (;) If I hadn't have been early, I wouldn't have seen the man who staggered out of the lift. He was holding a blood-stained handkerchief to his face and looked as if he was about to faint. A strange thought crossed my mind. Was he on the interview list before me? I offered to help him but he left the building muttering, 'No job's worth that.' When I looked at my watch, I saw my turn had come.
3 **A** The semi-colons could go in a number of places. It depends which sentences you want to show the reader are linked.
B It all began one year ago; in those 12 months he had changed so much.
4 **a)–b)** *Check your answer with your teacher.*

Pages 22–23: Using a full range of punctuation (L6–7)

5 **A** Go! Get Dad! Help!
Go get Dad? Help!
B Sarah said, 'Amy is bossy.'
'Sarah,' said Amy, 'is bossy.'
C After I left, Dave, Andy and Sam went to a party.
After I left Dave, Andy and Sam went to a party.
6 **a)–b)** *Sample answers:*
However, with little energy, or food, remaining, surviving this jungle adventure is not going to be easy, and this day is far from over. **OR** This day is far from over, however,

and, with little food, or energy, remaining, surviving this jungle adventure is not going to be easy. **OR** With little energy, or food, remaining, surviving this jungle adventure is not going to be easy, and this day, however, is far from over.

7 **a)** B
b) *Check your answer with your teacher.*

Pages 24–25: Improve the organisation of your writing (L5–6)

1

Words that give order to instructions	Words that show time in a story	Words that link ideas in an argument
finally, next, first, after this	*meanwhile, eventually, soon, afterwards, next*	*however, in addition, finally, despite this, in contrast*

2–3 *Check your answer with your teacher.*

Pages 26–27: Improve the organisation of your writing (L6–7)

4 *Check your answers with your teacher.*

5 **a)–c)** *Check your answer with your teacher.*

Pages 28–29: Improve your informative writing (L5–6)

2–3 *Check your answer with your teacher.*

Pages 30–31: Improve your informative writing (L6–7)

4 **a)–b)** *Check your answer with your teacher.*
c) different styles of trainers → variety of models
made bigger → extended
strong → sturdy
make them different sizes → half-size increments
heavy wear and tear → the most boisterous use

Pages 32–33: Improve your persuasive writing (L5–6)

1 **a)–b)** using a quotation – 'We hold these truths to be self-evident, that all men are created equal' (to give authority to your idea)

giving a positive idea – 'will be transformed into an oasis of freedom and justice' (to show your idea will be good)

repeating a phrase – 'I have a dream' (to build an impression in your audience's mind giving a personal example – 'my four little children' (to make your idea seem real or familiar to people)

giving a negative example – 'the state of Mississippi, a state sweltering with the heat of injustice, sweltering with the heat of oppression' (to show that things are not good now)

finishing with a short, dramatic point – 'I have a *dream* today!' (so that people will remember your idea)

2 *Check this with your teacher.*

3 **a)–d)** *Check your answer with your teacher.*

Pages 34–35: Improve your persuasive writing (L6–7)

4 **a)** yellow **b)** pink **c)** green **d)** blue

5 **a)** start **b)** positive **c)** point of view **d)** opposite **e)** choose

6 **a) i)** yellow **ii)** purple
b) To make them seem relevant to people's lives/make them seem real.

7 *Sample answers:*
Investing for a better future is an admirable idea. What better way to do that than by improving the facilities for young people in this area? They are the future, after all. Why has the council turned its back on the youngsters of this area? Does it think that if it ignores us, we will go away? Why should our problems be brushed under the carpet? We are the future, after all.

8 *Check your answer with your teacher.*

Pages 36–37: Improve your imaginative writing (L5–6)

1 **a)** story A
b) *Check your answer with your teacher.*

3 **a)** yellow – Carefully choosing words to create atmosphere.
green – Using phrases that help to control pace (speed).
grey – Using uninteresting background detail.
b) Carefully choosing words to create an atmosphere.
Using phrases that help to control pace (speed).
Showing off language skills through interesting images.
c) *Check your answer with your teacher.*

3–4 *Check your answer with your teacher.*

Pages 38–39: Improve your imaginative writing (L6–7)

5 **a)** 32 years old; one of the best car thieves on the Eastern seaboard; able to support himself as a car thief; been arrested repeatedly; never done time
b) *Sample answer:*
Strolling down the quiet side-street, Teddy Franklin was moderately attractive, but not handsome enough to turn heads. That

suited him. He stopped in front of a shop window to check out his reflection. A smug smile spread across his face as he looked at the expensive, fashionable clothes he thought he wore so well. As he walked on, he glanced back at his reflection, checked that he really did look good ... and that there was no one else in sight. His eyes slid back to the car he had spotted on the other side of the road. Casually, he strolled across, and did what he did best.

c) *Check your answer with your teacher.*

2–3 *Check with your teacher.*

Pages 40–41: Improve your writing to review (L5–6)

1 'I'm not old enough to vote but I'm old enough to have my say about ...'
'I wonder if Mary Forest has actually asked teenagers what they think about ...'

2 *Check your answer with your teacher.*

Pages 42–43: Improve your writing to review (L6–7)

3 *Check your review with your teacher.*